SIX NEW STUDENTS

FRANZ BRANDENBERG

illustrated by ALIKI

GREENWILLOW BOOKS

A Division of William Morrow & Company, Inc. • New York

2   3   4   5   6   7   8   9   10

Library of Congress Cataloging in Publication Data
Brandenberg, Franz.   Six new students   (Greenwillow Read-alone series)
Summary: The six Fieldmouse children find their new school
more enjoyable than they anticipated.   [1.   School stories.
2.   Mice—Fiction] I.   Aliki.   II.   Title.   PZ7.B7364Si   [E]
77-24883   ISBN 0-688-80124-2   ISBN 0-688-84124-4 lib. bdg.

T 3974

for Rebekkah and Jonas

CONTENTS

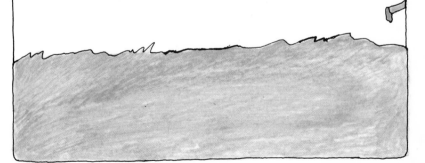

CHAPTER 1

"Time to get up, boys and girls!"
called Father Fieldmouse.
"It's the first day of school."

Annette, Bertrand, Colette,
Daniel and Esther
jumped out of bed.
Ferdinand pulled the covers
over his head.

"Anyone who doesn't want
breakfast may stay in bed,"
said Father Fieldmouse.
Ferdinand jumped out of bed.

"I wonder how our new school
  will be," said Annette.
"I don't like arithmetic."
"I won't either," said Ferdinand.
"I don't like calligraphy,"
  said Bertrand.
"I won't either," said Ferdinand.

"I don't like botany," said Colette.

"I won't either," said Ferdinand.

"I don't like art," said Daniel.

"I won't either," said Ferdinand.

"I don't like physical education,"
  said Esther.

"I won't either,"
  said Ferdinand.

"You'll love school,"
   said Father Fieldmouse.
"I doubt it," said Ferdinand.

After breakfast,
Mother Fieldmouse gave
the Fieldmouse children
their lunches.
"Sunflower seeds!"
they all shouted.
"Not again!"
"They are good for you,"
said Mother Fieldmouse.
"I love them,"
said Father Fieldmouse.
"We are sick of them,"
said the Fieldmouse children.

"You can have something different
tomorrow," said Mother Fieldmouse.

"Good-bye!" shouted
the Fieldmouse children.
"Have fun!" said Mother
and Father Fieldmouse.
"I won't," said Ferdinand.

CHAPTER 2

At school, Ferdinand sat
in the first row,
with the first graders.

Esther sat in the second row,

with the second graders.

Daniel sat in the third row,

with the third graders.

Colette sat in the fourth row,
with the fourth graders.

Bertrand sat in the fifth row,
with the fifth graders.

Annette sat in the sixth row,

with the sixth graders.

First they had arithmetic.

All the children except Ferdinand

got out their arithmetic books.

"I don't like arithmetic,"
  said Ferdinand.
"What do you like?"
  asked the teacher.
"I like to draw,"
  said Ferdinand.
"Then you may draw,"
  said the teacher.
  She gave him a drawing pad.

Ferdinand drew a big castle.

"That's a nice castle,"
said the teacher.
"It has so many towers."

"It has two small towers,
    two medium-sized towers,
    and two large towers,"
    said Ferdinand.
"How many towers altogether?"
    asked the teacher.
"Six," replied Ferdinand.

Next they had calligraphy.

All the children except Ferdinand

got out their pens.

"I don't like calligraphy,"

said Ferdinand.

"Perhaps you'd like to draw

some letters," said the teacher.

"I'd love that," said Ferdinand.

He drew all the letters
from A to Z.
When he was finished,
he drew them again,
in a different way.

Then they had botany.

All the children except Ferdinand

got out their botany books.

"I don't like botany,"

said Ferdinand.

"Perhaps you'd like to draw

this flower," said the teacher.

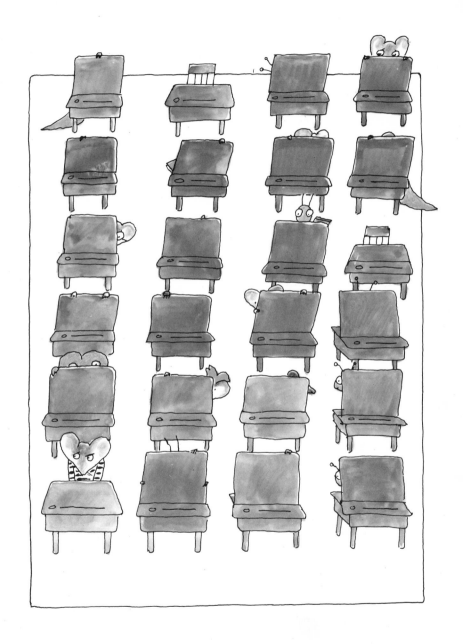

"I'd love that," said Ferdinand.
He looked carefully
at the flower, and then
drew everything he saw.

He drew
the stem,
the leaves,
the head,
the petals.

The teacher rang the bell.
"Lunchtime!" she called.
The children ran out
to the school yard.

CHAPTER 3

"What do you have for lunch?"
  the old students asked
  the Fieldmouse children.
"Sunflower seeds," they replied.
"We are sick of them!"

"We love sunflower seeds,"

said the others.

"What do you have?"

Annette asked the baker's daughter.

"Raisin bread," she replied.

"I am sick of it."

"I love raisin bread,"

said Annette. "Let's trade."

"What do you have?"

Bertrand asked the grocer's son.

"Tutti-frutti," he replied.

"I am sick of it."

"I love tutti-frutti,"

said Bertrand. "Let's trade."

"What do you have?"
Colette asked
the dairyman's daughter.
"A piece of cheese," she replied.
"I am sick of it."
"I love cheese,"
said Colette. "Let's trade."

"What do you have?"

Daniel asked the nut seller's son.

"Salted peanuts," he replied.

"I am sick of them."

"I love salted peanuts,"

said Daniel. "Let's trade."

"What do you have?"
  Esther asked
  the vegetable man's daughter.
"A big carrot," she replied.
"I am sick of it."

"I love carrots,"
  said Esther. "Let's trade."

"What do you have?"
Ferdinand asked
the fruit seller's son.
"A ripe banana," he replied.
"I am sick of it."
"I love bananas,"
said Ferdinand. "Let's trade."

Annette ate her raisin bread,

Bertrand ate his tutti-frutti,

Colette ate her piece of cheese,

Daniel ate his salted peanuts,

Esther ate her big carrot,

Ferdinand ate his ripe banana,

and all the others ate

their sunflower seeds.

CHAPTER 4

In the afternoon, they first had art.
All the children except Ferdinand
got out their drawing pads.
Ferdinand had his out already.
"I don't like art," he said.

"Never mind," said the teacher.

"Draw anything you wish."

"I'd love that," said Ferdinand.

He drew the whole school,

with everything in it.

Last, they had physical education.
All the children except Ferdinand
put on their sneakers.

"I don't like physical education,"
said Ferdinand.
"Perhaps you'd like to join
in the ball game," said the teacher.
"I'd love that," said Ferdinand.

CHAPTER 5

"How was school?"
asked Mother and
Father Fieldmouse.
"I didn't like arithmetic,
calligraphy, botany, art
and physical education,"
said Ferdinand.
"So, I didn't have to do them."

"What did you do?"
   asked Mother Fieldmouse.
"I drew a castle
   and added up its towers,"
   replied Ferdinand.

"That was arithmetic,"
    said Annette.
"If that was arithmetic,
    then I love it," said Ferdinand.
"I do, too, but I thought
    I didn't," said Annette.

"What else did you do?"
  asked Father Fieldmouse.
"I drew all the letters
  from A to Z
  in two different ways,"
  replied Ferdinand.
"That was calligraphy,"
  said Bertrand.
"If that was calligraphy,
  then I love it," said Ferdinand.
"I do, too, but I thought
  I didn't," said Bertrand.

"What else did you do?"
  asked Mother Fieldmouse.
"I drew a flower," said Ferdinand.
"Its stem, its leaves,
  its head, its petals."

"That was botany," said Colette.
"If that was botany,
  then I love it," said Ferdinand.
"I do, too, but I thought
  I didn't," said Colette.

"What else did you do?"
asked Father Fieldmouse.
"I drew the whole school,
with everything in it,"
replied Ferdinand.

"That was art," said Daniel.

"If that was art, then I love it,"
said Ferdinand.

"I do, too, but I thought
I didn't," said Daniel.

"What else did you do?"
  asked Mother Fieldmouse.
"We played ball," said Ferdinand.
"That was physical education,"
  said Esther.

"If that was physical education,
  then I love it," said Ferdinand.
"I do, too, but I thought
  I didn't," said Esther.

"I am so glad you enjoyed school,"
said Father Fieldmouse.
"And for lunch tomorrow
you can have anything you like,"
said Mother Fieldmouse.
"Sunflower seeds, please!"
shouted all the Fieldmouse children.